FREE DVD   **FREE DVD**

CDA Exam DVD from Trivium Test Prep!

Dear Customer,

Thank you for purchasing from Trivium Test Prep! We're honored to help you prepare for your AP exam.

To show our appreciation, we're offering a **FREE *CDA Exam Essential Test Tips* DVD by Trivium Test Prep**. Our DVD includes 35 test preparation strategies that will make you successful on the AP Exam. All we ask is that you email us your feedback and describe your experience with our product. Amazing, awful, or just so-so: we want to hear what you have to say!

To receive your **FREE *CDA Exam Essential Test Tips* DVD**, please email us at 5star@triviumtestprep.com. Include "Free 5 Star" in the subject line and the following information in your email:

1. The title of the product you purchased.

2. Your rating from 1 – 5 (with 5 being the best).

3. Your feedback about the product, including how our materials helped you meet your goals and ways in which we can improve our products.

4. Your full name and shipping address so we can send your **FREE *CDA Exam Essential Test Tips* DVD**.

If you have any questions or concerns please feel free to contact us directly at 5star@triviumtestprep.com. Thank you!

- Trivium Test Prep Team

Table of Contents

INTRODUCTION

The Dental Assisting National Board (DANB) was established in 1948 to ensure that dental assistants met educational requirements across the country. Its certification is required in 29 states for practicing dental assistants and recognized by 38 states. Standard exam fees are approximately $375 depending on the state you live in (some have fewer or additional fees).

The DANB is now available as an electronic exam at over 200 sites nation wide. It can be taken anytime throughout the year at a recognized testing facility. After applying to take the exam, you will be notified within approximately 4 weeks regarding your exam location and availability. There is a 60-day window allowed for you to take your test.

What is Needed to Take the Exam?

Dental assistants wishing to take the DANB must have graduated from a CODA-accredited program and include a copy of their certificate and school letter which includes their graduation date. Alternative applicants can test with documentation of a high school diploma or GED and documentation of at least 3,500 hours of work experience in the past 2 years as a dental assistant; or proof that they were a former DANB certified dental assistant. All applicants must also have up to date CPR certification.

On the day of the exam you will need to bring your admission notice and a valid ID. You will not be allowed to bring personal items such as phones, bags or purses. Restroom breaks are not included in the testing time, so if you must excuse yourself, the test time will continue to count down.

Exam Questions

There are 320 multiple-choice questions on the exam and is divided into 3 sections:
- General Chairside - 90 minutes, 120 questions
- Radiation Health and Safety - 75 minutes, 100 questions
- Infection Control - 75 minutes, 100 questions

General Chairside questions revolve around practical chairside knowledge such as collecting and recording clinical data, dental procedures, dental material preparation, lab materials, patient education, emergency prevention and office operations.

The Radiation section is primarily focused on the exposure and evaluation of dental x-rays but also includes film processing, mounting, radiation safety for the patient and staff, and radiation education.

Under the Infection Control portion, approximately 1/3 of the questions are based on occupational safety, while the rest focus on universal precautions, disease transmission prevention, asepsis and instrument sterilization.

Exam Results

Immediate results are given after your electronic examination in the terms of "pass" or "fail." Your results will show the number of answers that are correct and incorrect. The board has a predetermined standard of correctly answered questions, and will award a *pass* for each applicant who reaches this threshold.

Should you fail the exam, there is no limitation on how many times you can re-take it. At the closure of your exam, you will be notified of what sub-content area you will need to improve.

Your formal results will automatically be sent to state licensing agencies.

Chapter 1: General Chairside

Basic Oral Anatomy and Physiology

Permanent dentition: The adult mouth consists of 32 teeth: 8 incisors, 4 canine (also called cuspid or eye) teeth, 8 premolars, and 12 molars. Permanent teeth erupt approximately between the ages of 6-12. Wisdom teeth, the 3rd set of molars, typically do not erupt until closer to 17-21 years of age.

Primary dentition: Also called deciduous teeth, baby teeth begin erupting at approximately 6 months of age until age 6. There are 20 teeth in number - 8 incisors, 4 canine teeth, and 8 molars.

Mixed dentition: The stage in a child's mouth where a combination of both permanent and primary teeth can be found.

Maxillary teeth are found in the upper arch, while **mandibular** teeth are found in the lower arch. This can easily be remembered because the **maxilla** bone is what supports the maxillary teeth, and the jawbone or **mandible** is what supports mandibular teeth. Permanent dentitions have 16 teeth in each arch while primary dentitions have 10 teeth in each arch.

Each patient's mouth is divided into **quadrants**. The upper right, upper left, lower left and lower right. Each quadrant consists of one central incisor, one lateral incisor, one canine tooth, two premolars and 3 molars. The **anterior** teeth are the incisors and canines, and **posterior** teeth are the premolars and molars. The ADA uses the Universal Numbering System, which identifies teeth using numbers **1-32 for permanent teeth**, and letters **A-T for primary teeth**. The numbering begins at the patient's upper right posterior molar, continuing onto the left side, then down to the lower left posterior molar and continuing onto the right side, as if it were a circle. The International Standards Organization (ISO) numbering system is the one used by the World Health Organization (WHO) and numbers the teeth 1-8 in each quadrant, with the quadrants numbered 1-4. The Palmer Notation System is usually used in orthodontics and uses a number and bracket system to identify where the tooth is located and in what quadrant.

Anatomy

Teeth begin forming during the earliest stages of gestation, even before implantation of the fertilized egg into the uterus (zygote stage.) The teeth continue to develop throughout the rest of pregnancy and into childhood. Tooth formation begins with the **bud** stage, then progressing on to the **cap** and **bell** stage. Prior to the tooth erupting, this formation takes place inside of a sac.

The portion of the tooth above the gum lines is known as the crown, while the root is the portion that extends into the jawbone. **Enamel is the strongest material in the body**, and makes up the external portion of the crown, tapering off at the gumlines. **Dentin** is the layer under the enamel and the bulk of the tooth root. **Pulp or nerve tissue** is the inner layer of the tooth, which supplies nutrition and blood supply. **Cementum** is a thin layer of the tooth on the outside of dentin on the root of the tooth.

Anterior teeth have one root and one cusp per tooth while posterior teeth have 2-3 roots and anywhere from 2-5 cusps depending on the tooth and where it is located. Maxillary molars have 3 roots, while mandibular molars have 2 roots.

Each tooth has **5 surfaces**. These surfaces allow the dentist or practitioner to identify what portion of the tooth is involved with a restoration, decay or other finding. The surfaces are **mesial, distal, lingual, facial/labial/buccal, and occlusal/incisal**. Mesial surfaces are the side of the tooth that is closest to the midline, between the teeth. Distal refers to the surface of the tooth that is furthest away from the midline, also between the teeth. The term **interproximal** or **contacts** refers to the area between the teeth where their two surfaces touch each other, while the embrasure is the area just outside of the contact point. Lingual surfaces are those that are on the tongue side of the tooth, while facial/labial/buccal surfaces are those that are closest to the cheeks and lips, away from the tongue. The incisal surface is the biting edge of the anterior teeth, while the occlusal surface is the chewing surface on the posterior teeth.

Head and Neck Anatomy

The human skull has 8 cranial bones and 14 facial bones. Both the head and neck muscles and anatomical functions aid in the eating and digestion of food. 12 sets of cranial nerves are located in the face. The primary arteries are the internal carotid and the exterior carotid.

The mouth has 3 sets of major salivary glands that help lubricate the mouth and aid in digestion. These glands are the **parotid, submandibular and sublingual** salivary glands. The parotid gland is the one located in the posterior portion of the maxilla, adjacent to the first molars, and it is the **largest** of the 3 salivary glands. Saliva from this gland is excreted through the **Stensen's** duct. The Submandibular gland makes more than half of the saliva in the entire mouth, which is delivered through the **Wharton's** duct. The sublingual gland is the small gland that is located just under the front of the tongue, and excretes saliva through the **Bartholin's** duct.

Oral Diseases

Caries / decay is the term used to describe a cavity. Tooth decay is contagious and is usually caused by the bacteria lactobacillus and mutanstreptocci as well as poor oral hygiene and an poor nutritional choices. Decay can be halted in some cases. The beginning stage of decay is known as **incipient decay**, where the enamel has begun to decay but the cavity has not made it's way completely through the enamel to the dentin. **Overt decay** is decay that has reached through the enamel, into the dentin, and **rampant** decay is when there are numerous overt cavities present during the same period of time, typically due to neglect.

Type I **Gingivitis** is the initial inflammation of gum tissue caused by lack of oral hygiene, and is reversible. **Periodontal disease** occurs when gingivitis is untreated and results in the destruction of bone tissue and attached gingiva (periodontal ligaments). Pockets around the teeth will become deeper and more difficult to care for. Untreated periodontal disease will lead to tooth loss. Gum disease is also directly related to **systemic disease conditions** such as cardiovascular conditions, diabetes and premature labor. Type II Periodontitis is the period where gingivitis begins to morph into a periodontal disease state, causing irreversible damage that is evident by bleeding and swelling. Type III Periodontitis is more severe progression of periodontal disease, which is also accompanied by moderate bone loss and bad breath. Type IV Periodontitis is the advanced stage of the disease where tooth mobility has occurred due to severe bone loss, and may result in loss of the teeth due to the lack of supporting structures.

Oral Cancer as well as other pathologies can be detected by identifying tissues in the oral cavity that appear irregular. If abnormal tissue is found, the dentist may recommend a **biopsy** of the tissue to send off for testing. Tissues that appear to be white, red, raised, or different than the same area on the opposite side of the mouth are all signs that the tissue could be abnormal or precancerous. **Leukoplakia** is a term used to referr to white tissues or plaques on the soft tissue. **Candida** or *thrush* is an overgrowth of yeast bacteria in the mouth. **Lichen Planus** is a white, red, or open lesion area that is due to an autoimmune disorder.

Abnormal tissues outside of the oral cavity must also be noted. Lesions on the face, head and neck should be assessed and documented for future reference or proper referral. The ABC's of possible skin pathologies include Asymmetry (being present only one one side of the mouth or face), Border (is the border of the lesion well defined, or is it irregular?), Color (how does the color differ from the healthy tissue?), Diameter (measure the size of the lesion in millimeters), and Evolve (does the lesion change over time?) If any of these are noted to not be normal, referral or biopsy is necessary.

Systemic diseases or venereal diseases can also be present in the oral cavity. **HPV, herpes (simplex or zoster),** and symptoms of **HIV** may be evident upon clinical examination. The dental assistant cannot diagnose any disease conditions in the patient, but can take note of symptoms and make the dentist aware of them.

Gingivitis is the initial inflammation of gum tissue caused by lack of oral hygiene, and is reversible. **Periodontal disease** occurs when infection is untreated and results in the destruction of bone tissue and attached gingiva. Pockets around the teeth will become deeper and more difficult to care for. Untreated periodontal disease will lead to tooth loss. Gum disease is also directly related to **systemic disease conditions** such as cardiovascular conditions, diabetes and premature labor.

Charting

Red marks indicate treatment needs that are diagnosed and need to be completed, while **blue** marks on a patient's chart indicate the treatment has already been performed. **Amalgam** fillings are outlined on the tooth and colored in solid. **Composite** fillings are outlined. **Gold** restorations such as crowns or onlays are outlined and then marked with diagonal lines to indicate a precious metal. **Porcelain** crowns or onlays are simply outlined. **Stainless steel crowns** are outlined and then crosshatched (criss crossed). **Extracted or missing** teeth are marked with a large "X", while **impacted** teeth are circled.

Vital Signs

A patient's vital signs must be recorded at every appointment. The average vital signs for an adult are as follows:

Respiration: 12-20 breaths per minute

Pulse: 60-100 beats per minute

Blood pressure: Under 120/80

Chairside Dental Procedures

Understanding the layout and flow of care in the treatment area is what encompasses a majority of the dental assistant's skills. Helping the dentist practice is an efficient manner and always being one step ahead will improve the quality of patient care.

Four-Handed Dentistry Techniques

Before a patient can be seen, the operatory must be prepared with the proper equipment and instruments for the treatment that will be performed on that day. Selection of the proper tray setup and dental materials should be made and laid out for the dentist in the order that they will be used.

Patient Positioning

After escorting the patient back into the treatment area, record vital signs and review their medical history before covering them with a patient napkin and reclining them into the proper delivery position. The 3 chair positions include **upright**, where the patient is sitting up; **supine**, or laying flat on the back with head and knees level with one another; and **sub-supine**, for medical emergencies, where the patient is laying back with the head below the level of the knees. Position the light in the correct angle to maintain visibility. Always begin with the light directly over the patient's torso before turning it on. Moving the light slightly forward and angling it toward the patient's face will achieve **maxillary light positioning. Mandibular** light positioning will pull the light directly over the patient's mouth, with the beam pointed straight down toward the lower teeth.

Operator Positioning

There are 4 operator positions or zones: **Static (12-2 o'clock), Assistant (2-4 o'clock), Transfer (4-7 o'clock),** and **Operator (7-12 o'clock.** Procedure preparation will typically occur in the static zone. The assistant will sit in the assistant zone during treatments and the transfer zone is where instrument transfers are made, to protect the patient. Dentists will be seated in the operator zone. These zones will be different for left-handed operators, with the positions mirrored on the opposite side.

Instrumentation

When **transferring instruments**, the assistant should hold the instrument with the working end facing them, and the handle or non-working end should be placed directly into the dentist's hand. If receiving an instrument from the operator first, the assistant can use their last two fingers of their hand to retrieve the instrument from the operator, before placing the instrument into their hand.

Holding the HVE (high volume evacuator) tip is usually done using the thumb-to-nose or pen grasp. The thumb-to-nose grasp allows maximum control of the suction. During procedures, the HVE should be placed slightly distal to the tooth being prepared.

Keeping the treatment area accessible for treatment and vision is important for the operator. An operator will typically need a **fulcrum** to rest their working hand and improve stability. **Direct or indirect vision** will allow the operatory to see the area directly with their eyes, or reflected through their mirror.

Selection and Preparation of Armamentarium

One of the most important skills a dental assistant has is knowing what equipment is necessary for specific procedures. Every dentist had different ways they prefer their trays to be set up, but common setups include **basic (exam), restorative, crown and bridge,** and **emergency** trays.

Cotton rolls and **dental dams** are used to isolate teeth. A dental dams use hole punches sized 1-5 as appropriate for the tooth to be treated. 1 is the smallest and used for mandibular anterior teeth, and 2 is used for maxillary anterior teeth. Premolar teeth require a #3 hole punch and molars #4. A #5 hole is used for the anchor tooth or bridges. If root canal therapy is being performed, only one hole will be punched, otherwise 6-8 punches are recommended.

High-speed handpieces use burs for tooth preparation, while **slow speed handpieces** are used in prophylactic procedures, adjustments of some appliances, or in the laboratory. **Burs** are carbide or diamond, and come in 3 designs for being held by the handpiece: straight, friction grip, or latch. For restorations that require an outer wall, a **tofflemire** or **matrix band** is used. During fillings, the tooth will be adjusted with the necessary bur. Composite restorations will also require acid etch and a bonding agent.

Hand instruments are used for **carving, cutting, or exploring**. Exploring type instruments in a basic setup would include a mirror, probe, explorer and cotton forceps. Other accessories such as scissors, hemostats or articulating paper holders have specific uses that are accessed as needed.

The dentist administers **anesthetics**, but the placement of topical gel by the assistant helps minimize discomfort. Mandibular blocks are placed in the retromolar pad. Local anesthetics are packaged in **carpules**. The carpule contains the information regarding the drug, dosage and expiration date. Maxillary anesthetic administration typically uses infiltration around the tooth to be treated. **Vasoconstrictors** help the anesthesia last longer, and are displayed on the carpule in the form of 1:20,000 or other ratio to indicate the concentration of the solution. All needles should be removed in a safe manner and placed in a sharps container after use and to avoid needle sticks.

Nitrous Oxide can be monitored by dental assistance with the proper certification, but it may only be administered by the dentist. After the treatment procedure, assistants should place the patient on 100% oxygen for 5 minutes. Never leave a patient alone when they are on nitrous oxide, as a medical emergency may occur. **Oxygen** tanks are green in color, and **nitrous** tanks are always blue.

Assessments

There are 6 classifications of decay. Class 1- occlusal, class II-interproximal posterior, class III-interproximal anterior, class IV- incisal anterior, class V- marginal, class VI-cusps.

Monitoring of periodontal disease is performed with a periodontal probe. Gum pockets up to 3mm deep are considered healthy. If the patient has several deep pocket areas and evidence of infection, then periodontal disease is present and the patient will require periodontal treatments such as scaling and root planing.

Orthodontic evaluations determine how the patient's teeth bite together and if there is any type of malocclusion. Bite classifications include Class I (normal), II (overbite), or III (underbite). Occlusion is also checked after performing restorative procedures like fillings or crowns, using articulating paper, adjusting the restoration as needed. A **space maintainer** or **band and loop** are useful in pediatric dentistry to prevent orthodontic problems associated with premature tooth loss.

Tooth **staining** is often an aesthetic concern, but may have several causes and be an indication of tooth damage. **Intrinsic stain** cannot be polished off, and is due to either long exposure to outside factors or from damage to the tooth's nerve. Internal bleaching can be used to help reverse stain associated with nerve damage, or whitening products can help lift internal stain found only in the enamel. **Extrinsic stain** is typically from food or tobacco use, and can be polished off. Take home whitening trays are made by taking an impression of the patient's teeth and then fabricating a custom made tray for them to use, typically with a carbamide peroxide or hydrogen peroxide solution. In-office whitening accelerates whitening results by utilizing an ultraviolet light. Professional strength peroxide solutions can come as highly concentrated as 30-35%.

Treatment Specific Procedures

Endodontics, or root canal therapy (RCT), uses files or similar tools to remove diseased or damaged nerve tissues from inside of the tooth. The **canal is then sterilized** with water and sodium hypochlorite before being dried with paper points and then filled with a material such as **gutta percha**. It is necessary to place a crown over the tooth after RCT is completed. If reversible pulpitis exists, conditioning sedatives can be placed over the pulp in an attempt to avoid RCT. The term *endodontics* is also used to describe the dental specialty that focuses on the treatment of diseases in the tooth nerve.

Extractions can be surgical or simple. The selection of instrument will be determined based on which tooth is to be removed. **Impacted** teeth are those teeth that have not broken through the bone and are lodged into place due to adjacent teeth or lack of space. Some complex extractions may be performed by an oral surgeon. Oral and maxillofacial surgeons are specialists that perform advanced surgical procedures treating disease, injuries or abnormalities of the mouth, head and neck.

Dry sockets may develop if a blood clot fails to form or stay in place. Placing a **surgical dressing** in the socket (or other surgical area such as one treated with periodontal surgery) can help protect predisposed sites to infection and aid in recovery. After surgical procedures, the assistant may perform **suture removal** at the follow up appointment if non-dissolvable stitches are used.
Should severe infections result in a dental emergency, the dentist may perform an incision with a **scalpel** to drain the area, such as one with a severe abscess.

Amalgam fillings are made up of a mixture of mercury, silver, tin and zinc. A **triturator** will mix the amalgam carpule, and an amalgam carrier helps transfer the material to the tooth. Burnishers or carvers will help shape the filling to the tooth. In some cases a **temporary filling** may be used to treat a dental emergency, or prior to crown application on a tooth that has received root canal treatment.

Primary teeth or teeth that are waiting on a permanent crown will have a **temporary crown**, typically a stainless steel crown. The crown's margin should be trimmed for a proper fit. Temporary crowns are seated using temporary cement. **Permanent crowns** and **bridges** are porcelain, gold, or porcelain fused to gold and is seated using permanent cement. This occurs after the tooth has been prepared, **a final impression** for restorative purposes has been made, and the dental laboratory has fabricated the permanent restoration. Some types of **cement** include glass ionomers, resin based cements, and zinc-based cements.

Dental **impressions** are used to fabricate single tooth, multiple tooth, or full mouth restorations. **Alginate** impressions are one of the most common types taken. Casts or **models** of the teeth are then made from the impression, and are used for study, provisional restorations, custom appliances, and other treatments. Metal or plastic **stock trays** come in various sizes and are used for primary impressions. Lower trays are "U" shaped, with a cutout for the tongue, while upper trays cover the area near the roof of the mouth. **Edentulous** trays are used for denture impressions. **Sectional** trays are chosen when only one area of the mouth needs to have an impression taken, such as for a final crown impression.

A full **denture** is made after the patient has had all of their teeth removed and adequate healing has occurred. **Immediate dentures** are made prior to the removal of the teeth, and placed immediately after the extractions. **Dental implants** are made of titanium, which is highly biocompatible. The implant root is placed surgically into the bone and allowed up to 6 months of healing prior to uncovering the implant to place the abutment and permanent crown. **Mini implants** are placed and immediately covered with the prosthesis or appliance.

A *pediatric* dentist is a dentist that focuses on the treatment and care of teeth from birth through adolescence. *Periodontists* care for the health of the connective tissue around the teeth, such as in patients that suffer from periodontal disease, bone loss and gum recession. A dentist that focuses on the restoration of teeth by using prosthesis such as removable dentures or permanent appliances is called a *prosthodontist.*

Preventive Procedures

Depending on where the dental assistant is licensed, it may be within your jurisdiction to perform preventive therapies such as coronal polishing and sealant application. **Coronal polishing** uses a prophy angle and slow-speed handpiece to remove stain and plaque biofilm from the surfaces above the gumlines. **Dental sealants** protective layers over the occlusal surface that prevent decay and make the area easier to clean. To apply a sealant, the tooth must first be conditioned using acid etch and rinsed. After the clear sealant material has been brushed onto the tooth, it is cured with a light.

Fluoride applications can be performed using a **topical gel** or **varnish**. Gels are applied using foam trays, while varnish is brushed on in a small amount. Varnish stays in place longer, but creates a temporary film on the tooth.

A **prophylaxis** is a routine preventive cleaning that removes plaque and tartar from the teeth. If there are severe areas of tartar and bone loss, then **scaling and root planing** are necessary. Both procedures are performed by the hygienist, using ultrasonic instruments and hand scalers or curettes to remove the debris. **Gum flap** or **crown lengthening** periodontal surgeries may aid in the treatment of severely diseased areas by aiding in the removal of calculus and increasing the patient's access to the area.

Chairside Dental Materials

Impression Materials

Impression materials are mixed on a paper pad with a spatula or in an extruder. **Alginate** impression material comes in powder or liquid forms, and is used for making "non permanent" types of appliances or study models. The material is an **irreversible hydrocolloid** and must be mixed thoroughly with the proper amount and temperature of water for the proper consistency. In addition to preliminary alginate impressions, the other type of impressions is **final impressions**, which are used for fixed appliances like crowns or bridges. This type of impression is extremely accurate and sent to the laboratory for the fabrication of appliances or restorations. Final impression material is very durable and is usually one of the following types: **Polyether** - uses two tubes of material and is auto mixed from a machine; **Polysulfide** - also stored in two tubes as a base and catalyst; **Polyvinyl Siloxane** - stored in two guns or a putty; and **Bite Registration** - used to recreate the relationship between the upper and lower arches to help determine the relationship of a restoration against the opposing arch.

In addition to previously mentioned stock, edentulous and sectional trays, there are also disposable, triple and custom trays. **Disposable** impression trays are for single use, and may come in full arch or quadrant sizes. For recording final impressions and bite registrations, **triple trays** allow the final impression and bite registration to be taken at the same time. An **acrylic** tray is for custom impressions of a patient's arch for the use of creating prosthetics like dentures.

Cements

For temporary crowns, provisional restorations, or sedative purposes, **temporary cement** can be used, typically lasting up to 6 months. Temp Bond and **zinc oxide eugenol** (ZOE) are common temporary cements. **Permanent cement** is used when seating the final restoration, like a permanent crown or bridge. They are meant to be long lasting and anti-cariogenic. **Glass ionomer**, resin cement, polybycarbonate and zinc phosphate (must be mixed on a glass slab) are common permanent cements.

Bases and Liners

Bases and liners are used to protect the nerve of the tooth that has been prepared or a restoration, or to encourage the growth of dentin. **Bases** like glass ionomers are useful because they release fluoride that bonds to the tooth structure and is compatible with all types of restorative materials. ZOE can be used as a sedative for the pulp but are not compatible with resin materials due to the clove oil that is a key ingredient.

A dentin **liner** is used to help protect the nerve from irritation under restorations like fillings. **Calcium hydroxide** is most commonly used as a dentin liner because it promotes dentin growth and is compatible with all restorations. **Varnish** is applied over a liner to help seal the tubules of the tooth.

Acid Etch

Etch conditioning opens the tubules of a tooth to aid in the bonding of material to the enamel or dentin. Only a short application time is needed before the tooth is rinsed and dried thoroughly, leaving a chalky appearance.

Bonding

Porcelain and composite materials can microscopically bond to the layer of a conditioned tooth. During the preparation, the tooth may secrete an oily layer called the **smear layer**.

Direct Restoration Materials

Amalgam, composite and glass ionomer restorations are direct, because they are performed in a single appointment and directly into the tooth.

Amalgam fillings are held in place by physical retention or chemical bonding. Their application requires the amalgam carrier, carver, burnisher, and articulating paper. A tooth treated with an amalgam filling may experience recurrent decay, amalgam tattoos and micro leakage.

Tooth colored **composite** fillings are bonded directly to the enamel and help retain strength and natural tooth enamel due to less tooth preparation. The material is placed on in layers and is light cured. Mylar strips may be needed depending on the location of the filling. Composite restorations can be matched to the shade of the teeth and release fluoride, preventing recurrent decay.

If a **glass ionomer** filling is used, the mixing directions must be followed very carefully. The restorative material has many diverse uses as it can improve aesthetics as well as be used for buildups and cement. It will bond to enamel or dentin and comes in a variety of shades. An advantage of glass ionomers is that they release fluoride over time, making it anticariogenic and prevent possible recurrent decay in the area.

Indirect Restoration Materials

Indirect treatments require two or more visits, like dental crowns and bridges. While some restorations can be created in-office using advanced equipment, most involve cast restorations that are made at a dental laboratory.

Crowns made of **gold** are much more durable to excess grinding or clenching, while **porcelain** crowns are more aesthetically pleasing. **Inlays** and **onlays** or "three-quarter crowns" are similar to crowns that do not cover the entire tooth and they may be made of gold or porcelain. **Stainless steel** crowns are used on children's primary teeth or as a temporary crown on a permanent tooth. A temporary **provisional** crown may be needed after a dental emergency or to protect a tooth, and can be made of custom acrylic or be preformed.

To perform a crown, the gum tissue must be retracted using **retraction cord**. The cord is gently placed below the gums to retract the tissue, and may be braided, unbraided, and comes in different sizes.

Laboratory Materials

Study models of the teeth are made from dental impressions to create non-fixed appliances like retainers, whitening trays or night guards. **Plaster (model plaster)** is used to pour the model when you are making diagnostic casts or working on preliminary treatments. **Stone** is harder than plaster and is used when making dentures, athletic guards, night guards, retainers or bleaching trays. **Die stone** is the hardest stone, and is used by lab technicians for making permanent restorations. When pouring the material into an impression, it should be poured very slowly from one side to the other, in order to prevent bubbles in the model. A vibrator can help shake bubbles out of freshly poured models and create a smoother result.

When you have your finished model, you can use a **model trimmer** to reshape the study model into the appropriate form. If you are making whitening trays, a **vacuum former** will suck down the plastic material over the study model, to create a customized fit.

Other laboratory equipment includes a **lathe**, which is used for polishing temporary crowns and gold materials. Instruments found in the dental lab will include lab knives, mixing bowls and spatulas, rag wheels, polishing disks and mixing surfaces.

Patient Education and Oral Health management

The dental assistant plays an important role in the education of oral hygiene, postoperative care, and nutritional habits of patients.

Fluoride

Adults and children (who can expectorate thoroughly) should use a pea-sized amount of fluoridated toothpaste twice each day. Overexposure to fluoride from swallowing toothpaste or elevated concentrations of the mineral in the water can cause fluorosis of the enamel. The enamel is strong but may be brown or pitted. Topical fluoride can help teeth remineralize and resist decay. Prescription fluoride is also effective in treating gingivitis and sensitivity.

Pre and Post Treatment Instructions

Providing patients with pre and postoperative instructions will help to make their treatment successful and aid in recovery. If the patient is taking prophylactic antibiotics or oral sedation medication, they should be instructed to take the prescription 1 hour prior to their scheduled appointment.

Patients that are receiving **sedation** services should not eat prior to their appointment, and limit their clear liquids. After surgical procedures like extractions or gum flap surgery, recommend the patient stick to a **soft diet** as healing occurs. Patients who undergo extractions must also not smoke or drink through a straw for at least 24 hours so that proper blood clotting can occur. Pressure from a cause can be applied until initial bleeding stops, and a tea bag can also be used.

Plaque Control Techniques

Toothbrushing should be performed using a soft toothbrush using light pressure, for 2 minutes twice each day. The Bass method of toothbrushing teaches adults to angle their brush 45 degrees toward the gumlines, making small strokes across one or two teeth at a time. This helps remove plaque below the gumlines. Children can use the Fones method, which is brushing in small circular strokes focused on one tooth at a time. Disclosing tablets or agents can be used to evaluate plaque control methods and increase effective removal.

Flossing must be performed at least once each day to remove plaque between the teeth. It does not matter if it is waxed or unwaxed, both types of floss remove plaque similarly. Water flossers, floss threaders and proxa-brushes are also effective tools for cleaning areas that are hard to reach.

Saliva will aid in the development of pellicle on the surfaces of the teeth within just a few minutes. Plaque develops along the gumlines and if not removed will trigger gingivitis, which is the inflammation of the gum tissue around the tooth.

Calculus is the result of calcified or mineralized plaque bacteria on the surface of the tooth. It cannot be removed using conventional oral hygiene methods and must be removed with an ultrasonic, curette or scaler.

Untreated gingivitis can lead to the infection spreading deeper into the gum pockets and bone, resulting in periodontal disease and tooth loss. Periodontal disease is directly linked with systemic health conditions

Nutrition

Drinking tap water can ensure that patients receive the proper intake of fluoridated water. Municipal water supplies keep an optimum concentration of fluoride at .7 to 1.2 ppm, which is adjusted in the summer and winter based on people's water intake habits. Bottled water does not have regulated fluoride levels.

To strengthen the teeth, calcium absorption can be increased when combined with vitamin D. **Xylitol** is a 5-carbon sugar that repels plaque (s. Mutans) and is linked with stronger teeth. Crisp fruits and vegetables stimulate gum tissue and circulation. A healthy amount of carbohydrates can aid with the repair of diseased periodontal tissues.

Foods that lower the pH of the mouth can increase enamel decalcification, which begins at 5.5pH. Juice, soda and sports drinks all lower the pH and increase the likelihood of developing decay if they are consumed on a frequent basis.

Prevention of Emergencies

Medical Emergencies

The most important step to preventing a medical emergency from occurring in the dental office is to perform a thorough **health history** screening at each appointment, as well as record vital signs. **Abnormal vital signs** may be a precursor to emergencies such as cardiovascular attacks.

Follow up with the patient to see if they have taken their **medications** as prescribed, such as insulin, blood thinners or blood pressure medication. White coat syndrome is common in dental offices, meaning that patient's blood pressure is elevated due to anxiety. If the patient is **asthmatic**, ask them to keep their inhaler at hand during their appointment.

Signs of a **stroke** include headache, problems walking, talking, or being understood, as well as partial paralysis or vision difficulty; contact EMS immediately. **Seizures** may be predicted in advance as some people experience an "aura." If a patient seizes, keep them safe by removing all equipment and instruments from their immediate area. **Heart attacks** may be identified by chest pain/pressure; difficulty breathing; numbness of the arms; nausea; fatigue; perspiration; and body discomfort.

Almost every medical emergency recommends the patient be placed on 100% oxygen, except for someone who is hyperventilating. Place the patient in a comfortable position, or if they are unconscious they should be placed in the **supine** position, so that blood flow can reach their vital organs like the brain and heart. Patients that are choking should be given abdominal thrusts until the foreign object is expelled.

The A-B-C's should always be checked during an emergency: **airway, breathing, and circulation**. The American Red Cross recommends that these signs be checked in the order of "C-A-B" instead of the traditional A,B,C. Check the patient's pulse. If they have no pulse, immediately begin CPR. Airway and breathing are assessed after chest compressions have begun. To make sure the airway is open, perform a head-tilt chin-lift and then place your ear over the patient's mouth to check for air flow. **Look, listen and feel** for the air. If no air flow is evident, deliver air flow using a device such as a bag-valve-mask that prevents pathogen transfer. The use of an **AED** can increase the patient's likelihood to recover from their emergency. Most AEDs will have voice prompts that guide you through the process, with CPR alternating with any necessary shock deliveries. All staff members are required to have CPR certification.

An office emergency plan and **emergency drug kit** should be made available to all staff members. The kit will contain emergency medications used for things such as allergic reactions (Epi-pen and Benadryl) , heart attacks (nitroglycerine) and diabetic syncope (icing, or another form of sugar).

Dental Emergencies

If a patient hemorrhages during a surgical procedure, pressure should be applied immediately. Patients that are on medications such as prescription **blood thinners** or aspirin can experience uncontrollable bleeding during procedures like extractions. The patient should not discontinue taking their medication without the consent of their doctor. Their primary care physician should be consulted prior to scheduling surgical procedures.

Never leave a patient unattended that is receiving **nitrous oxide**. A patient may become nauseous to the point of vomiting, or become unconscious. **Drug overdoses** can occur when medications are not prescribed or used in the proper amounts.

Some patients may experience allergic reactions to materials or equipment used in the dental office. **Latex** gloves are one of the most common sources of allergens, and the patient may have a small to severe reaction. Nitrile glove use can prevent this from occurring.

Should a foreign object such as a restoration or piece of equipment fall into the patient's throat, do not attempt to retrieve the object unless you can see it. If you can see the object, a finger sweep can help to remove it. Broken instruments may require the use of an x-ray to indicate the specific location, and at all times aim to keep the patient calm.

Office Operations

Supply and Inventory Control

Keeping an **inventory** of items that are ordered, how often, and the amount needed can help to manage the amount that is necessary for the practice to run efficiently. Some offices use spreadsheets or inventory cards. Items should be placed **first in, first out** on the shelves, to prevent items from expiring. When placing large orders from suppliers, a **purchase order** is sued, and a packing slip will show what items were delivered or were placed on backorder. All hazardous material will have an **MSDS sheet** that accompanies the product. The MSDS sheets should be saved in the appropriate OSHA binder and the biohazard labels should be placed on any secondary containers that contain the product.

Patient Reception, Communication and Accounting

At a patient's first appointment, they should complete a health history questionnaire and patient registration form. The patient's **treatment plan** will show prescribed dental needs as well as an estimate of any insurance benefits that they may have. When the patient is to be treated, they must sign a **consent form** to state they are aware of why the treatment is being performed and what side effects may accompany it. . Good communication regarding the treatment plan is an important step that is needed to help the patient truly understand why prescribed treatment is necessary for the improvement of their oral health. A **practice management software** is a computerized treatment planning program that can help manage patient records, treatment needs, ledgers, and appointment history.

Information may be filed alphabetically (most charts are stored this way), chronologically (insurance claims) or geographically. **Recall systems** help maintain a record that identifies when patients are due for their next prophylaxis. Most recall systems are done through the mail, telephone or electronic (advanced.) For the most part, all recall patients should be seen every 6 months for preventive care appointments. The

retention of a patient refers to the office's ability to keep the person as an active patient, rather than one who leaves the practice for any variety of reasons.

A patient's **ledger** shows what services have been performed and the amount of money due. If the office participates in their own financing program, a federal Truth in Lending form is used to identify that payments will be extended 4 or more months. The office's **day slip** helps record what monies have been collected on a particular date. If a patient has a **balance** on an account, the past-due categories are 30-60 days, 60-90 days, and over 90 days.

Dental **insurance claims** are made using ADA CDT (Code on Dental Procedures and Nomenclature.) Every dental procedure has its own CDT code. Clearing houses will process electronic or paper claims.

Legal Aspects of Dentistry

Dental assistants are not to provide any services or procedures that are reserved for the dentist or hygienist. Only the dentist may place fixed restorations, such as the cementing of a permanent crown. Adjunctive procedures must be done under the supervision or direction of the dentist. **General supervision** involves activities can be performed when the dentist is not on site, while **direct supervision** encompasses activities that must be performed while the dentist is in the office.

Basic ethics should be maintained. Patient **confidentiality** that respects a patient's privacy will prevent their information from being shared with other patients or people outside of the office without the patient's consent. **HIPAA** is the adopted health insurance act that ensures a patient's privacy.

When a patient gives **informed consent**, they are saying that they have been informed of the procedure, risks and possible side effects. The **standard of care** is the treatment that would be recommended by other dentists treating the general dental patient. **Documentation** in the patient's records should be thorough. If something is incorrect, draw a line through it and initial it.

Chapter 2: Radiation

Expose and Evaluate Radiographic Films

Taking quality radiographic images is essential for dental care providers. Without accurate films, the dentist cannot diagnose pathology like interproximal decay, impacted 3rd molars or periodontal disease. The angulation and positioning of films in the patient's mouth, as well as the processing techniques used, dramatically affect the quality of care that the patient receives.

Select appropriate radiographic techniques

Different types of radiographs show the operator various perspectives of the teeth, oral structures and anatomy. The way these films are taken are typically one of two different techniques: bisecting the angle and paralleling.

Bisecting the angle is the traditional method used for taking dental x-rays. The film is held with a device such as a snap-a-ray and placed as close to the tooth as possible, attempting to get the film parallel with the long axis of the tooth. Because they may not be parallel, it is necessary to draw an imaginary line that bisects the angles of the film and the tooth. Then, direct the x-ray beam **90 degrees toward this imaginary angle.** If the angle is incorrect, **foreshortening** or **elongation** of the image will occur.

The **paralleling technique** uses a film mount system such as an XCP. Each mount is assembled based on what teeth are to be radiographed - anterior PA, posterior PA, and bitewing. Each mount uses a bite block, which holds the film, a locator ring, and an indicator arm. The bite block is placed further away from the tooth to enable the film to be placed parallel to the tooth. After the patient bites down on the block, the locator ring should be as close to the face as possible, which increases film quality. The x-ray tubehead is aligned with the indicator rod and locator ring.

Select appropriate equipment for radiographic techniques.

Most patients will have their intraoral films taken with a paralleling device (XCP). The **paralleling technique is the preferred method for taking dental radiographs.** In the cases where the patient has a severe gag reflex or is unable to bite down on the device, then it may be necessary to use a film holder (snap-a-ray) or hemostat to hold the film in place for the bisecting the angle technique to be used.

Intraoral film comes in different speeds and sizes. The most commonly used **speeds are D and E**, with D being used most of the time, but E requires less radiation. Film sizes come in 1-5 that are used as appropriate for taking PAs, interproximal x-rays, and occlusal films as well as additional films that are necessary for panoramic and cephalometric radiographs.

Each intraoral film is enclosed in a waterproof casing. Inside of the film is a piece of lead foil, and a black paper slip with the film located between the folded black paper. The lead foil keeps radiation from exiting through the back of the film and entering into the patient's surrounding tissues. **Lead foil** must be disposed of according with state and federal regulating agencies.

Dental x-ray machines are usually mounted on the wall, but they can also be portable. An extension arm allows the tubehead to be moved around the patient. The **tubehead** contains the necessary components for emitting x-rays while an enclosed aluminum filter barricades weaker wavelengths from leaving the housing. At the end of the tubehead is the cylinder, when is used to align the direction of the beam. **Cylinders** come in lengths of 8 (**short**) or 16 (**long**) inches. Made of lead, the cylinder only allows straight beams to be aimed toward the patient and film, preventing radiation scatter. Every b**eam is restricted to 2.6 inches**, so it is important to have angulation accurate in order to avoid cone cutting the image on the film. Cone shaped cylinders are no longer used as they cause scattered x-ray beams. Only circular or rectangular cylinders should be used, as these only allow for straight beams, which result in decreased exposure to the patient.

X-ray beams are caused by electrons being produced from a tungsten filament inside the cathode of the tubehead. Negative electrons from the tungsten filament are sent to the anode, which causes a collision and the creation of heat and x-rays. The only x-rays to escape the tubehead are those that go through the aluminum filter (stronger waves), collimator, and straight through the position indicating device (PID).

The **control panel** allows the operator to adjust exposure based on the type of film being taken, speed of film, and size of the patient. The exposure time, mA and kVp should be checked to guarantee that the quality of image would provide the best results. The kilovoltage (**kVp**) is adjusted accordingly based on the physical characteristics of the patient (their bone size and body density.) **87** kVp is used on most adult x-rays, and increased to **90** for someone of a heavier build or bone density. A lower kVp of **70** would be appropriate for a child. Milliamperage (**mA**) will be between 10-15 mA and is selected, but the majority of the time a 10 mA is used.

Select infection control techniques and barriers to minimize cross-contamination in the operatory according to ADA/CDC and OSHA guidelines

Cross-contamination between the patient, x-ray equipment and the treatment area can easily occur if infection control procedures are not followed appropriately. In addition to wearing PPE, the operator must also ensure that all equipment that comes into contact during the process does not become contaminated. All surface areas such as countertops, darkroom equipment and tubeheads must be wiped down. Tubeheads and controllers must be draped with a barrier of some sort to prevent saliva contamination. Even lead aprons and the chair that the patient is seated in should be wiped down with a hospital grade disinfectant.

The positioning indicating devices (such as XCP or snap-a-ray) must be sterilized after every use. It is recommended that heat sterilization is used, but they can also be disinfected using immersion in a cold sterile glutaraldehyde solution. Panoramic bite blocks should be covered with a disposable barrier, or else sterilized or disinfected using the same method as other positioning devices.

After an intraoral film has been taken, the contaminated film must be handled correctly in order to avoid transferring bacteria to the processor and dark room.

> *If using a darkroom:* Place used films inside of a clean cup and use that cup to take the exposed films into the darkroom. While wearing gloves, open each film packet and allow the film to drop into a clean cup or paper towel. Remove your

contaminated gloves and then place the films into the machine one by one using your bare hands.

If using a daylight loader: Daylight loaders can easily become contaminated due to the fabric sleeves, so it is important to have disposable film packets around each x-ray. The exposed x-rays should have the barrier removed from them as they are dropped into a clean cup, without touching the film with your gloves. After the contaminated barriers have all been removed and discarded, the cup with the clean films can be placed inside of the daylight loader. This prevents transmission of any saliva to the loader. *OR,* if disposable covers are not available, place each contaminated film into a clean cup, remove your dirty gloves and then put the cup into the daylight loader (avoiding the sleeves). Put on clean gloves and then unwrap each film. Remove your soiled gloves and then load each film into the processor (this prevents glove powder from damaging the image.) After taking your hands out of the sleeves, open the lid up and remove all of the contaminated trash.

Select patient management techniques before, during, and after radiographic exposure

Have the patient remove any jewelry, oral appliances (such as a denture or partial) and glasses. These can create ghost images on or interfere with beam contact to the film.

All patients should be draped with a **lead apron** and **thyroid collar** when having radiographs taken, which prevents excess radiation exposure to vital and reproductive organs. Ask the patient to keep their head against the headrest, to prevent movement and film distortion. The position or angulation of their head will depend on what type of film is being taken. Maxillary films are best taken with the patient's ala-tragus line parallel to the floor, and mandibular films should have the chin slightly elevated where the line between the tragus and corner of the mouth are parallel to the floor.

Gagging is a common concern for patients with sensitive gag reflexes. Keep the patient as calm as possible, asking them to breath out of their nose. Taking the x-ray as fast as possible will benefit the patient. Some people find it helpful to place salt on the tongue, rinse with cold water, or use distraction techniques like elevating their foot.

Take care to ensure there is no movement or shaking of the tubehead during exposure, as this will result in a distorted image.

Expose dental films, using various techniques.

The angulation of the tubehead will determine whether or not the x-ray will have the correct image and if it is not distorted. *Horizontal angulation* is the side-to-side relationship of the tubehead toward the film. The beam cannot be angled; otherwise overlapping of the teeth will result. *Vertical angulation* is the up-and-down position of the x-ray beam to the film. If the tubehead is angled upward, it will decrease the angulation, and if it is angled downward it will increase the angulation. Vertical angulation is important, as it will vary based on what area of the mouth is being radiographed. For maxillary films, the tubehead is usually angled downward (20+ to 45+ degrees), and for mandibular films it is usually angled horizontally or slightly upward (0 to -20 degrees).

An FMX will consist PAs of the incisors, cuspids, bicuspids and molars. The film should be placed in the mouth with the distal half of the tooth mesial of the tooth to be radiographed included on the image. For example, a premolar bitewing should also include the distal portion of the canine tooth on the film. This allows for the visual inspection of the mesial contact area of the first premolar. A PA should include the long axis of the tooth and the periapical area of the root, with the tooth or teeth centered in the middle of the film.. PAs are useful for diagnosing any anomalies around the tooth such as abscesses, root canal treatment guidance, and bone loss. Bitewing (BWX) films are placed centered along the occlusal plane and are used for viewing the interproximal areas of the premolars and molars to detect cavities between the teeth, health of restorations, and initial bone loss. The paralleling technique is preferred for PA films, but for bitewings it is appropriate to use either the paralleling or bisecting-the-angle techniques.

Panoramic films are used to assess the eruption patterns of the patient's mouth, as well as jaw anatomy, bone quantity and other structures like the nasal sinuses. Viewing the sinuses is important as it can detect swelling against the root structures, or amount of bone present for patients who are considering dental implant therapy. Orthodontists may use cephalometric films to see a profile of the patient's skull and how it relates to facial features and oral function. Occlusal films are larger intraoral films that are primarily used to assess the eruption patterns of anterior teeth in pediatric patients.

Edentulous patients (those without any teeth), or partially edentulous patients still need to have radiographs taken to provide a clear analysis of oral structures and screening for pathologies. Occasionally, patients that have palatal tori may have difficulty having intraoral radiographs taken, due to the large amount of excess bone in their mouths.

The film should be placed as close to the tooth as possible. If the film is too far away from the tooth, a **penumbra** will exist. Penumbras are distortions on the film that decreases sharpness, shape of the tooth, and overall clinical quality of the film.

Evaluate radiographs for diagnostic value

After processing the films, it is important to check whether or not the film's quality is diagnostically beneficial. The **contrast** seen on the film image is the amount of shade variation seen on the film. Adjusting the kV on the tubehead controls changes the contrast of the image. **Density** is the darkness of the film, and can be affected by the patient's anatomy, distance of the tubehead from the patient, or controlled using the mA settings. The correct density and contrast are important for the film to have any diagnostic value.

When reading the film, areas that appear white or blank on the film are called **radiopaque.** An example of radiopacity on an x-ray film would include where an amalgam filling is present, or the variation of bone and dental structures that prevented the x-ray beams from reaching the film. **Radiolucent** areas on the images are those portions on the film that are darker, where beams went through spaces or less dense bone, and made contact with the x-ray film.

Common problems seen on films are:

Cone cut: Due to inappropriate angulation, resulting in a blank area on the film.

Overlapping: Overlapped interproximal areas between the teeth, due to inappropriate horizontal angulation.

Foreshortening or elongation: Images that appear too long or too short due to inadequate vertical angulation

Placement: Does the film show all areas of the appropriate teeth? Are any teeth left out (such as 3rd molars)?

Blank film or partial image: Not exposing the film, or exposure to a light leak.

Image is too dark or too light: Inappropriate exposure times, kVp, or developer chemicals mishandling.

Blurry image: Movement of the tubehead of patient during exposure.

Fogged image: Old film or inappropriate safety lighting can damage the image quality.

Blotchy, streaked film: A dirty processor and rollers can leave streaks, speckles or stains on the film.

Lines or creases in the film: Bending the film, or pushing on it with fingernails will create damage in that area of the image.

Spots on the film: Splatter from developer or air bubbles can cause spots on the final image.

Ghost images: Not removing appliances like dentures can interfere with the x-ray beam.

Radiographic Solutions

To process a radiographic image, 3 solutions are needed. These are the **developer, fixer and water**. The developer and fixer are typically found in concentrate forms, which are then placed into the processing tanks. The **developer** is the chemical that affects the silver halide crystals to create a dark image (radioluscency) on the final film. The **fixer** (ammonium thiosulfate) removes any remaining unexposed crystals from the film, creating a clean, clear portion of the image (radiopacity.) After the unexposed crystals are removed, the film is then dipped in the water tank to cleanse the film of any remaining chemicals, thereby preventing additional chemical changes that will affect the image.

Film Processing

Each type of film processing follows a **Developer-Rinse-Fixer-Wash** cycle. Chemical levels should be checked each day, as evaporation may occur. Oxidation of older solutions will also compromise film quality.

Manual Processing

Traditionally, x-ray films were processed manually in dip tanks. This method may also be needed from time to time for one reason or another. Each type of film has specific directions for the temperature of solutions as well as how long the film should be dipped in each solution tank. The warmer the solution, the shorter the length of time that the film should be dipped into the tank (**warm solutions will process the film faster**.) Manual processing takes **longer** to perform than automatic processing.

Automatic Processing

Automatic x-ray processors are much **more efficient** than manual processing, and typically take around 5 minutes to complete. **Endodontic** cycles are also available on electric processors, allowing dentists to process a lower quality film in around 2 1/2 minutes for endodontic procedures.

Radiographic Infection Control

The same infection control steps should be taken during film processing as those used for handling dirty dental instruments. Cross-contamination can easily occur on equipment used for radiography unless proper infection control is practiced. For instance, films should be wiped off before being placed through the armholes of a daylight loader. Otherwise, pathogens will deposit themselves on the openings and contaminate the operator's hands/arms each time the machine is used.

PPE should always be worn during film processing. Not only to prevent cross-contamination to the operator, but to protect the operator from harmful chemicals during processing.

Storing Chemical Radiography Agents

Properly **store chemical agents** used in radiography procedures according to the local regulatory agency, in compliance with the OSHA Hazard Communication Standard.

Solution Disposal

Properly **dispose** of all chemical agents and other materials used in dental radiography procedures. After the solutions have been used numerous times, they must be discarded, otherwise the quality of the films will be compromised. Change solutions every 3-4 weeks. Follow local OSHA and governmental restrictions regarding hazardous material disposal. When refilling the reservoirs, always **fill the fixer tank first**, preventing fixer from contaminating the developer tank.

Quality Assurance

Films can vary in image quality if the processing chemicals and procedures are not performed correctly. Common mistakes or alterations to the image include:

Static electricity - In dry climates, or when moving rapidly during processing, films can have a crackled or lightning shaped image appear on the final film from static electricity exposure during the loading process. This occurs when unwrapping the film, before placing it into the developer.

Dark images - When a film is put in the developer for too long or the solution is too warm, the crystals on the film will become over processed.

Light images - Not developing the film for a long enough time will cause the crystals to not process enough and wash away. This can also occur if the developer is too old, or too cold.

Blank (or partially blank) films - Light leaks in the darkroom or daylight loader will result in a completely blank area on the film.

Mount and Labeling of X-Ray Films

It is extremely important to mount dental films in the proper manner, to prevent inaccurate diagnosis locations in the patient's mouth. When looking at an FMX mount, there are anywhere from 18-20 slots available to mount films. This includes 4 upper molar PA films, 4 lower molar PA films, 4 Bitewing films, and 6-8 anterior PA films. Labial (facial) mounting places the films in the same direction as if you were looking directly at the patient's mouth from the front. Special care should be taken to make sure the x-rays are not placed in the mount backward. The dot on the films should always be facing upward (pimple, not a dimple) to prevent the images from being reversed.

As you go about selecting which films to place in what location, you will identify factors such as the following film characteristics and anatomical structures to help you know which film goes in what location:

- Place the film with the dot bumping upward. If the dot is a dimple, then the film is backward.
- To better tell molar PAs upper from lower, remember that upper molars have 3 roots and lower molars only have 2.
- Upper films will have larger areas of radiolucency, due to sinuses and the nasal fossa.
- Lower molar films will show the external oblique ridge and mandibular canal.
- Generally the overall appearance of an FMX will reflect an upward curvature (smile).
- Restorative materials like amalgam and gold will appear radiopaque on the film. Use these images to help identify their location based on comparing the film the patient's chart. Open spaces are in turn, radiolucent. Natural structures such as bone and tooth enamel will have varying shades of radiopacity.
- If a patient is fully or partially edentulous, then anatomical landmarks like the maxillary tuberosity and corner of the eye socket can be used.

Monitor strips (stepwedge) with aluminum layers can be taken to monitor the quality of the images.

Care of the automatic processing machine is also essential to prevent damage or irregular processing of the films. Cleaning rollers and gears keeps the processor running correctly.

Film Duplication

Duplicating an intraoral film is important if the image needs to be sent to an insurance company or specialist office. Some film packets include 2 films (double pack), which omits the need to create a duplicate. The double pack film is typically only used when you know that there will need to be a copy made.

Traditional films are duplicated using **duplicating film** and a **duplicator** device. This machine is used in the darkroom and exposes a bright light onto the original x-ray film that in turn is transferred to the duplicating film. The film must still be processed in the developer and not exposed to daylight.

Radiation Safety for Patients

When x-ray beams pass through tissue, the tissue absorbs the energy from the beam. This absorption can cause molecular breakdown and disruption. **The tissues most affected by radiation** are reproductive cells, bone marrow, small lymphocytes and internal mucosa. In contrast, muscle and nerve tissues are the least affected. **Lead aprons and thyroid collars** should have lead that is at least .25mm thick in order to protect sensitive tissues and reproductive organs from scatter radiation.

Always use **ALARA** (as low as reasonably achievable) when determining how much radiation or how many x-rays to expose on the patient. Does the patient's concerns or risks warrant the amount of radiographs to be taken? Typical dental radiographs expose patients to only very low levels of radiation and almost all of the time does not cause a risk to the patient's health. However, the dentist should only prescribe x-rays as necessary to benefit the patient's oral health. Biological risk is determined as rem = rad multiplied by the Quality Factor (Q.)

Radiation effects are **cumulative**, meaning that they can occur over time and may not exhibit symptoms immediately after an exposure. A **latent period** can occur which allows time to go by before any symptoms of radiation damage are evident. The latent stage ends when the signs of damage first occur.

There are different forms of measurement used to describe radiation exposure and dose. The term used to describe exposure to radiation is **roentgen** (R). A **rad** is the amount of **radiation dose that is absorbed** (think "radiation absorbed dose.") Ultimately, one R of exposure will equal out to one rad. The International System of Units (SI) uses the term **gray** (Gy) instead of rad. 100 rad is equal to 1 gray (or 0.01 Gy is equal to 1 rad). The **effective dose of radiation** is known as **Rem**, while the SI dose is known as the **sievert** (Sv.) 100 Rem is equal to 1 Sv (and 0.01 Sv is equal to 1 Rem.) The **curie** is the measurement of radiation that is given off by radioactive material.

X-ray tubeheads that deliver over 70 kVP should have an **aluminum filter** that is at least one inch or 2.5cm thick. The filter helps prevent weaker x-ray beams from making their way out of the tubehead with the rest of the stronger beam. On the outside of the tubehead is a **collimator** that restricts the size (and shape) of the beam that comes into contact with the patient. This size should be restricted to **2.75 inches.** A **rectangular** collimator can further reduce radiation exposure but may result in an increased rate of cone cutting. **Cone** shaped collimators should *not* be used, as they result in excess scatter radiation.

Position indicating devices (**PID**) are used to control the direction of the beam. PIDs should be longer, at least 12-16 inches, because they encourage the straight beams to be used for exposure and reduce scatter radiation.

Radiation Safety for the Operator and Staff

Dental operators should follow the ALARA method of radiation exposure: **as low as reasonable achievable**. Do your best to minimize your exposure to potential radiation beams. As long as proper precautions are taken, dental operators can safely expose dental radiographs to their patients on a recurrent basis. However, if precautions are not followed, radiation exposure may exceed the **maximum permissible dose**. For a dental professional, the occupational worker MPD is **5 Rem** each year.

It is possible for the operator to monitor their amount of radiation exposure by wearing a radiation-measuring device. These devices are typically in the form of a **badge**, but may be in the form of another type of dosimeter. Utilizing proper working equipment that is not outdated will reduce scatter radiation.

To protect oneself from excessive occupational exposure, the operator should stand at least **6 feet** away from the tubehead. It is also important to stand at an angle that is not in the direct path of the x-ray beam. Do not stand in front of or directly behind the beam, but instead, stand at an angle that is 90-135 degrees to the tubehead, which is where the primary beam is being dispersed. The operator should never hold a mounting device or film in place for the patient during an exposure. Always use a film holder or have the patient steady their own device for themselves. Do not hold the tubehead, as scatter radiation will leak out during the exposure.

Using a shield device or radiation barrier can further reduce any scatter radiation that you could be potentially exposed to. Most of the time this is achieved when the operator exits the room to press the exposure button on the other side of the operatory wall. Simply wearing a lead apron while also being in close proximity to the tubehead is not considered safe, as cumulative radiation can affect areas that are exposed and not covered by the apron.

Patient and Dental Health Care Worker Education

Taking radiographs on a patient exposes both the patient and the health care worker to possible exposure of infectious diseases. Practicing universal precautions and using barriers along with proper disinfection of sterilization is important to keep pathogens from being spread from one person to the next.

Panoramic machines should have bite placement guides that are removable and can be disinfected by either cold sterilization solutions or conventional methods. Or, a barrier can be placed over the bite guide and then removed after use, with the bite guide being disinfected with a hospital grade surface decontaminant. The chin rest and handles should also be cleaned.

Surface disinfection of **lead aprons** with a wipe or spray prevents the transfer of pathogens due to saliva droplets from the x-ray procedure. A common mistake is using contaminated gloves to move the apron, and not cleaning the area of contact, causing it to be spread between patients.

Exposure **switches** should be covered with a barrier and/or be cleaned with a disinfectant after each use. **Bitewing and PA** film holders like the XCP or Snap-a-ray devices must have the entire appliance sterilized between uses. Some of these may melt in a traditional autoclave, so cold sterile solutions may be more appropriate. Even though this equipment is considered for non-invasive use, the same precautions should be taken as if it was equipment from a clinical treatment tray.

The dental health care worker should use **PPE** when taking x-rays, to prevent exposure of pathogens to themselves or the patient. In addition to PPE, it is important for all health care workers to be **immunized** against infectious diseases such as Hepatitis B.

Never handle used x-ray equipment or films without gloves. Disposable covers can be used to prevent contamination during processing procedures. Failing to practice proper infection control and barrier methods prior to loading will cause the daylight loader or other machinery to become contaminated, and potentially spread infection to the next person who is processing x-rays. If the film needs to be disinfected, only use hospital grade tuberculocidal surface disinfectants.

Patients should understand that radiographs allow the dentist to diagnose areas that are not visible during clinical examinations. Examples of findings that are only visible on radiographs include: abscesses, impacted teeth, missing teeth, supernumerary teeth, bone loss, decay, TMJ disorders, bone disorders, cysts, tumors, sinus complications and eruption patterns.

Chapter 3: Infection Control

Standard and Universal Precautions and the Prevention of Disease Transmission

Proper precautions taken during patient treatments, and handling equipment, can prevent the exposure and transmission of infectious diseases. Bodily fluid and blood can allow for diseases like HIV, Hepatitis, Staph, Herpes or Syphilis to be spread, so handling equipment that has been contaminated after use on a patient is important for the protection of the care provider as well as other patients.

Universal Precautions

Treating all bodily fluids as if they were infected with bloodborne pathogens helps prevent people from coming into contact with materials that are infectious. Since it is not always possible to know if someone has an infectious disease or not, all materials that come into contact with bodily fluid of any sort should be treated as if it were infectious. Proper PPE like gloves, masks and treatment gowns act as a barrier to guard the employee from exposure. Universal precautions was changed to "standard precautions" in 1996.

Standard Precautions

The CDC recommends that all bodily fluids except for sweat, tears, urine, nasal secretions, feces and vomit (*unless they visibly contain blood*) should be considered infectious. This includes blood, saliva, breast milk, cerebrospinal fluid, amniotic fluid, other internal fluids and non-intact skin or mucous membrane exposures. Standard precautions are used for every patient at all times and are defined by the CDC as:

"A set of precautions designed to prevent transmission of HIV, Hepatitis B virus (HBV), and other blood borne pathogens when providing first aid or health care. Under standard precautions, blood and certain body fluids of all patients are considered potentially infectious for HIV, HBV and other bloodborne pathogens"

While standard precautions and universal precautions are essential the same in regards

39

for the protection of patients and staff, universal precautions aim to prevent contact with potentially hazardous material while standard precautions focus more on expanding the definition of possible pathogenic substances. Both practices are aimed to raise the awareness of the practitioner concerning possible contamination sources and minimize their risks of transmitting diseases.

Maintaining Proper Hand Hygiene

Practicing proper hand hygiene is an important step in standard precautions. Washing the hands thoroughly with soap and then patting them dry, or using an antimicrobial agent such as an alcohol hand rub are both effective means of hand decontamination. A practitioners hands should be washed before entering and after leaving the treatment areas, and when visibly soiled by bodily fluids. Even when gloves are to be worn, the hands should be washed first. Having a sink with a foot-activated tap can prevent contamination of any knobs or handles, but otherwise a disposable hand towel can be used to turn the faucet on or off.

Personal Protective Equipment

Masks should be used to prevent airborne contamination from droplets or aerosols. The masks should be fluid resistant. Because damp masks will have decreased filtration capabilities, masks should be discarded after they are visibly moist and after each patient.

Using eye protection prevents injury or contamination to the eye during patient care. The glasses or face shield should be disinfected after each use.

Gloves must be worn during all clinical procedures and their use does not prevent the need for hand washing. To prevent disease transmission, do not touch any areas in the treatment environment with soiled gloves without using overgloves or removing the gloves first.

Shoes should have closed toes to prevent injury from accidentally dropped materials or sharp instruments. Lab coats prevent splatter from coming into contact with the practitioner, and should be changed when they are visibly soiled or repeatedly contaminated. Never wear lab gowns or coats outside of the clinical area.

Infectious Diseases

Most infection control procedures are to protect against bloodborne viruses like HIV and Hepatitis B or C. These viruses can be transmitted through contact with mucous membranes or blood, which the dental practitioner can be exposed to. Appropriate vaccination of healthcare workers can, along with standard precautions, prevent their risk for becoming infected from diseases like Hepatitis B. Tuberculosis is not typically as common, but because of its ease of transmission and the difficulty it takes to kill the bacteria on surface areas, most surface disinfectants and wipes are judged on their effectiveness on tuberculocidal microorganisms. MRSA (staph) is a difficult to kill bacteria that can cause significant infections on the surface of the skin. In some cases, MRSA bacteria can thrive for weeks in some environments.

Should a healthcare worker experience an occupational exposure to infectious diseases, such as through an accidental needle stick, then appropriate wound care should be taken immediately, followed by prophylactic care from their medical provider. The wound should be washed with soap and water while squeezing it to encourage bleeding and flushing of potential pathogens. Proper documentation of the exposure must also be recorded.

Prevent Cross-Contamination and Disease Transmission

Measures taken to prevent cross contamination are essential, as there are lots of potential exposures that can be used to transfer microorganisms. From properly handling patient records, to using disposable barriers, an efficient cross contamination prevention routine will prevent the transmission of pathogenic bacteria.

Chain of Infection

 Pathogens are disease-causing microorganisms. The risk of infection depends on the cycle known as the chain of infection.

Virulence — Number of Microorganisms — Susceptibility of Host — Portal of Entry

Virulence refers to the strength of the microorganism in its ability to cause a disease infection. The higher the quantity of pathogens that the host is exposed to, the more likely the host is to contract the disease. In order for someone to potentially become

41

infected, the pathogen must be highly virulent, in an adequate supply, and have a means of entry into a host (person) that will be susceptible to the disease. For instance, immunocompromised patients are more likely to become infected with certain infections than those of otherwise healthy individuals. This is why it is so extremely important to prevent infected materials or environments to come into contact with other patients or care providers. Utilizing barrier methods, PPE, sterilization processes and practicing proper hand washing can break the chain of transmission from one host to another.

Avenues of Transmission

Transmission of pathogens in the dental offices is allowed through different ways. Those that are relevant to dental providers include: ***Direct, indirect, airborne, aerosol, parenteral and bloodborne.***

Direct contact also known as person-to-person contact. This is when the pathogen is transferred from the host directly to the other person through touch. Indirect contact involves the person touching something that was contaminated with the pathogen, such as handling used equipment or touching contaminated surfaces with bare hands.

Airborne transmissions are also called *droplet* transmission, and are caused by droplets of moisture, which house the microorganism and travel through the air, from respiratory sources like when someone coughs. Similarly, aerosols, sprays and splatter are different sizes of airborne droplets that can be inhaled or contaminate the area around the source. Aerosol is a fine mist and can cause respiratory infections, but spray and splatter are able to travel at a farther distance than aerosols.

When transmission is made through a cut or puncture, it is considered parenteral, because it is through the skin. A bloodborne transmission occurs when an infected individual's blood or body fluid is transmitted through direct contact.

Maintain Aseptic Conditions

By using aseptic techniques, it is possible for the dental care provider to prevent the passing of pathogens to the patient or sites that could harbor bacteria. They key to prevent microorganisms from being passed from one person's oral cavity to other potential hosts is to have aseptic habits that are implemented and prevent the cross-contamination process from occurring.

Aseptic practices also prevent pathogens from being introduced to the patient's oral cavity. Because the patient's oral mucous membranes are exposed during routine dental care, and invasive procedures may be performed, avoiding the transfer of microorganisms to them is the only way to prevent them from becoming a host to the pathogen. If the body's natural barriers such as mucosa are compromised, the host can be placed at risk to contamination.

Avoid touching surfaces that can easily become contaminated. For instance, a foot activated water faucet can prevent microbial transfer after hand washing. Keeping the hands held upward allows other possible pathogens to drain down the arm instead of back onto the hand, before putting sterile gloves on.

Washing hands before and after procedures, wearing gloves, PPE, packaging sterilized instruments, and using disposable barriers or equipment are essential. In addition to items that have direct contact with the patient, surface areas such as the patient chair or countertops in the treatment areas should be thoroughly disinfected immediately after dismissing the patient.

Some of the most commonly used disposable barriers include those placed on light handles, syringe sleeves, chair covers, and x-ray controls. In some cases it is better to use disposable items if they would be hard or impossible to keep clean during regular use. Common disposables include prophy angles, suction tips, gauze, or needles.

In addition to protective equipment remaining aseptic, the practitioner should also prevent cross-contamination from used PPE. A new mask should be used for each patient, and replaced if it becomes soiled or moist. Do not re-use exam gloves, instead, use overgloves on top of exam gloves to touch anything that cannot be disinfected during your procedure, such as handling a medical chart.

Donning and removing your PPE should occur in a careful sequence so as to not prevent your hands from spreading microorganisms when not necessary. The first PPE item to be removed should always be your gloves. After washing your hands, then you can remove your protective eyewear, mask, and lab coat. Once these have been removed, you should wash your hands again thoroughly.

Perform Sterilization Procedures

Appropriate sterilization is necessary to completely eliminate pathogenic microorganisms from dental instruments. The sterilization area should be a separate location from the treatment area, and set aside for only instrument processing purposes.

Levels of Instrument Contamination

There are 3 levels of instruments as far as sterilization needs: *Critical, Semi-Critical, and Non-Critical*. Instruments that are used for invasive procedures like scalings, extractions, or come into contact with blood are considered critical. If the instrument is used in the mouth, but doesn't contact the bone or used to penetrate tissue (such as a mouth mirror), but still comes into contact with saliva or blood, is considered semi-critical. A non-critical instrument is something that does not come into contact with mucous membranes and tissues. After use, the instruments must be transported correctly to the sterilization area before they are cleaned, packaged and sterilized.

Types of Sterilization

All used instruments must be handled using PPE during the cleaning, packaging and sterilization process. Once the packaged instruments have been sterilized, they should remain bagged and be stored in a clean area until use. *Autoclaves, chemiclaves and flash sterilization* are all appropriate mechanical sterilization processes for dental office use. Autoclaves use pressurized steam to penetrate the packages and destroy spores or other microorganisms. Most autoclaves run at a cycle of half an hour, 15-20 psi at 250 degrees. Chemiclaves take the same amount of time at 20 psi and 270 degrees, but use chemical vapor steam and can create an unpleasant odor, which requires appropriate venting in the sterilization area. If an instrument is needed very quickly, then flash sterilization can be used. To perform flash sterilization, the instruments must be unwrapped to use in the 3-minute cycle of 270 degrees at 15 psi.

Cold sterilization uses liquid germicides to sterilize instruments that are heat sensitive and might otherwise melt in a traditional mechanical sterilizer. The use of an EPA steriliant or disinfectant should be used to immerse the instrument for as long as 10 hours prior to being needed for use (the time may be less for certain FDA defined high level disinfectants). After removing the instrument from a cold sterile solution, it must be rinsed thoroughly and used immediately or packaged for future use.

Dental handpieces require special steps to ensure proper sterilization and prevention of cross-contamination of bacteria. Because the mechanical portions of the handpiece cannot be pre-soaked or rinsed, the handpiece should be wiped down with a bactericidal wipe to remove debris and visible contamination. To remove any pathogenic bacteria from inside of the handpiece, flush the piece for 20-30 seconds before removing it from the water line. The handpiece can then be packaged and sterilized using steam or chemical processes, but should never be immersed.

Monitoring

To ensure that sterilization machines are effective, routine monitoring should be performed in the office on a regular basis. This provides an accurate assessment of whether or not the machine is performing properly. There are three different ways you can monitor your machine's performance: physical, chemical and biological. Physical monitors use indicators like those seen on color changing packages or tape, which shows the machine has reached the necessary temperature. A chemical monitor contains chemical indicators that will react to different environments. One portion (indicator) is put on the outside of the sterilization package, while the other portion (integrator) is enclosed in the bag with the instruments. OSHA has mandated that every office perform biological monitoring on a weekly basis for every sterilization machine that is used. This level of monitoring ensures that had to kill bacillus stearothermophilus spores or bacillus subtilis spores are completely destroyed during the appropriate sterilization procedure.

Environment Asepsis

Zones

Different zones in the office help keep microorganism exposure constrained to certain areas. The sterilization area must have defined clean and dirty zones for instrument processing. Instruments can be moved from the clean zone to the contaminated zone, but contaminated items may never be transferred to the clean zone, as this would destroy the aseptic chain.

Food must never be eaten in areas such as treatment rooms or instrument processing area. It is not hygienic and can pose a risk to the employee. Foods must also be stored in a separate refrigerator than the one that is used to house any dental materials used in the office.

Treatment Rooms

The treatment area including the patient chair, mechanical housing/mounting units, countertop surface and other areas that may become contaminated during patient care should be thoroughly disinfected between each patient. Hospital grade **tuberculocical** germicidal wipes or sprays are adequate to destroy microorganisms on these work surfaces. Adequate supplies of the germicidal product must be used, as there have been some studies, which suggest not using enough wipes in a hospital environment may actually contribute to the spread of deadly microorganisms such as **MRSA**. You do not want to spread pathogens from one area to the next in an effort to save money on a few germicidal wipes. Wipe the areas thoroughly and allow them to dry completely prior to handling them. According to the CDC, handpieces and air water syringe tips must be cleaned and sterilized to destroy any internal microorganisms that may be spread between patients, and external disinfection is not adequate.

Barrier use is an essential part of practicing an aseptic technique in the treatment area. Barriers prevent moisture from penetrating the plastic barrier and contaminating the surface below, keeping it free of pathogenic microorganisms. Common examples of areas that utilize barriers include the x-ray exposure button, light handles or an intraoral camera. Removing contaminated barriers should be done using gloved hands, and the dirty gloves should be disposed of with the barriers prior to touching the areas again and contaminating the surface.

Flooring such as laminate is easier to keep clean of splatter or fluids. Carpet is not easily cleaned and therefore is in appropriate for use in the clinical areas or sterilization zones.

Dental Labs

The dental laboratory can easily contribute to cross-contamination of supplies or patient prosthesis if supplies are not cleaned and asepsis is not practiced. Any product such as a crown, denture or impression, which has been in the patient's mouth, must be disinfected prior to handling it in the dental laboratory facility. After adjusting the prosthesis or restoration with laboratory equipment, it must once again be disinfected prior to it being handled in the treatment area for delivery into the patient's mouth.

Waste Management
Different levels of waste include:

General - Most waste in the dental office is general waste. It is not hazardous or regulated, and can be discarded of in normal wastebaskets.

Contaminated - If a product has come into contact with blood, such as suctions or gauze, it is typically disposed of with general waste. However, some states do place tighter restrictions on this level of waste.

Hazardous - This waste poses a risk to other people and the community. It may include toxic materials, like lead foils or removed amalgam fillings.

Infectious (Biohazard) - Blood-soaked material, sharps, and pathological tissue are capable of transmitting disease and must be disposed of in the appropriate biohazard container. Sharps must be disposed of in a puncture-resistant container that is completely closable.

State, local and federal regulations will determine exactly what type of disposal is necessary, as some locations are stricter than others in regard to their requirements.

Occupational Safety

What is OSHA

OSHA (Occupational Safety and Health Administration) is the federal organization that is set up to ensure the safety of employees under the direction of the US Department of Labor. Standards and guidelines put in place by OSHA help protect healthcare workers from common risks and exposures that they may come into contact with while caring for patients.

Blood-born Pathogens Standard

The **bloodborne pathogens standard** is to help protect employees from bloodborne diseases such as Hepatitis B (**HBV**), Hepatitis C (**HCV**), and **HIV** that can occur when working with sharps, needles or through other **occupational exposure**. Exposure plans made by the employer can provide the employee with the proper training and equipment needed to avoid occupational exposure to these diseases.

Healthcare workers must have **free access to the Hepatitis B vaccine** with the costs covered by their employer. The Hepatitis B vaccine is delivered in 3 doses over a period of time. Practicing universal/standard precautions and the appropriate disposal of sharps and infectious waste help protect the employee from injury. Employees must wear personal protective equipment to avoid exposure to infectious material, and all employees in the office must be trained appropriately regarding OSHA standards.

Hazard Communication Standard

A written list of hazardous chemicals must be kept in a central location in the office. All chemicals must have their **MSDS** sheets stored in this location so that employees can access the information regarding their hazardous risks. These sheets are beneficial for instances that involve chemical exposure and information is needed regarding the specific chemical's effects.

Occupational Exposure

An exposure is when an employee is injured by a sharp instrument such as a needle, or has had contact with potentially infectious fluids through a mucous membrane (such as the eye) or broken skin. These exposures have the capability of transferring diseases such as HBV, HCV or HIV. All fluids except sweat should be considered potentially infectious. If blood is not visible it is less likely that disease transmission will occur, but a proper medical professional should still evaluate the exposure.

If the employee has been vaccinated for HBV, they are not considered at risk for infection. An unvaccinated employee is 6-30% likely to contract HBV through a cut or needlestick, according to the CDC. On the other hand, HCV contaminated blood is only 1.8% likely to transfer the disease through a needlestick. HIV infected blood is only 0.3% likely to cause an infection when needlestick accidents occur.

Needlesticks are one of the primary sources of exposure. Proper handling of sharps is essential in order to avoid the risk of sticks with a used needle. Recapping a used needle should be done correctly, or with the use of a recapping device to avoid potentially sticking the other hand during recapping. Do not recap a needle using two hands, but instead use a one-handed scoop technique if a recapping device is not available. Used needles should not be bent after their use. All needles should also be properly disposed of in puncture-proof, sharps disposal containers.

PPE like gloves, masks and eyewear can prevent the exposure of bodily fluids to the mucous membranes or skin. Even after gloves have been removed, proper hand hygiene that includes thorough washing must be practiced.

Injuries should be properly documented, listing the date and time of the exposure, how it occurred, details about the type and amount of exposure and information about the patient (source) if it is known. Post-exposure steps as well as the employee's vaccination history must also be included in the documentation. All employees must also be provided with the appropriate, confidential counseling following their exposure, and be evaluated for illnesses after the event.

After the Exposure

After an occupational exposure has occurred, the skin at the area of the injury should be thoroughly washed with soap and water. The area of puncture should be squeezed to encourage bleeding and outward flushing of the pathogen if possible. If the eyes were exposed, they should be flushed thoroughly with water at an eye wash station. A physician that has experience in antiretroviral treatments should be contacted and seen for an evaluation of the exposure and recommend any necessary prophylaxis treatments. HIV testing is conducted immediately after the incident and then again at 6 weeks, 12 weeks and 6 months after the exposure. Physicians must consider:

- *The type of exposure that occurred*
  Was it something that came into contact with broken skin, a needlestick, mucous membrane or a bite?

- *The amount and type of the source of exposure*
  Was blood present, or a fluid like saliva that may have contained smaller traces of blood?

- *Known infectious status of the exposure*
  Was the patient known? Did they have a documented infection like HBV, HCV or HIV?

- *The employee's susceptibility*
  What vaccines did the employee previously have? What is their current immune status?

Types of Infections

Acute - An infection that results in a sudden onset of severe symptoms but only lasts for a short period of time.

Chronic - An infection that lasts for a long period of time, possibly for life.

Latent - A delayed response or dormant infection that causes symptoms after the exposure to the pathogen. The symptoms may be persistent, coming and going over time, such as symptoms associated with the herpes virus.

Opportunistic - When an infection occurs from a typically non-pathogenic microorganism, usually due to a compromised immune system in the exposed host. For example, elderly patients or those battling autoimmune diseases are more likely to contract infections and diseases than their otherwise younger or healthier counterparts.

Categories of Employees

There are 2 categories of employees in the dental field that are addressed in the bloodborne pathogens standard.

Category I –
An employee that performs responsibilities that places them in direct contact with blood or potentially infectious materials. This would include staff in the treatment area like the assistant, hygienist, or sterilization tech.

Category II –
An employee that doesn't normally have a job role that involves blood exposure but has the potential to be involved in a task that involves the risk of exposure. Front office employees would fall under this category as they don't typically interact in the treatment area, but may from time to time need to float through locations in the office or be involved in an emergency.

Once an employee has been assigned to job roles under one of these categories, the employer should provide proper vaccination services within 10 days of the job assignment.

Ionizing Radiation Standard

X-ray machines and equipment must be kept in restricted areas that limit the exposure of employees and other people in the office. Radiography equipment and rooms must have proper signage to indicate that radiation is being used in the area. Healthcare workers that are responsible for exposing radiographs must wear some type of radiation monitor on their body like a dosimeter or badge to oversee the amount of radiation that they are exposed to.

Exit Routes Standard

Emergency exits must be accessible to the employees as well as a posted diagram of evacuation routes from the building. Fire exits should have proper signage and remain unblocked by furniture or debris should an emergency occur and require evacuation of the building.

Electrical Standards

Electric equipment has proper safeguards, which must be taken if they are used in areas containing hazardous material. For instance, chemical film processors will require special installation and electrical wiring.

Chapter 4: Practice Test Questions

1. Which tooth is not found in the primary dentition?
    A) 2nd molar
    B) Canine
    C) Lateral incisor
    D) Bicuspid

2. A gold crown has just been completed. How should it be marked in the patient's chart?
    A) Outlined in red, with diagonal lines
    B) Outlined in red, with cross hatches
    C) Outlined in blue
    D) Outlined in blue, with diagonal lines

3. During a crown preparation, the assistant who is suctioning will be seated in what treatment area?
    A) 12-2 o'clock
    B) 2-4 o'clock
    C) 4-7 o'clock
    D) 7-12 o'clock

4. You are punching holes in a dental dam to perform an endodontic procedure on tooth #8. What size hole punch is needed?
    A) #2, 3, and 4
    B) #2
    C) #3
    D) #3, 4, and 5

5. A patient has decay on tooth #4, located on the highest points of the occlusal surface. What classification of decay does this patient have?
    A) Class I
    B) Class IV
    C) Class V
    D) Class VI

6. Which of the following is likely to cause severe extrinsic staining?
   A) Tetracycline
   B) Elevated systemic fluoride
   C) Smoking
   D) Genetic predisposition

7. What instrument is used to move amalgam from the mixing dish to the tooth?

   A) Amalgam carrier
   B) Beavertail
   C) Football burnisher
   D) Carver

8. The protective layer over the occlusal surface of a tooth, which repels decay and improves oral hygiene practices:

   A) Topical fluoride
   B) Fluoride varnish
   C) Coronal polishing
   D) Dental sealant

9. Which type of impression material is extremely accurate and is used to make dental crowns?
   A) Alginate
   B) Irreversible hydrocolloid
   C) Polyether
   D) Bite Registration

10. What type of material cannot be used as a base as it contains clove oil and prevents bonding of a permanent restoration?
    A) Zinc oxide eugenol
    B) Varnish
    C) Calcium hydroxide
    D) Glass ionomer

11. Which type of restorative material is held in place by retention?
    A) Glass ionomer
    B) Amalgam
    C) Composite
    D) Resin

12. What type of stone or plaster should be used for the fabrication of a permanent porcelain crown?
    A) Die stone
    B) Model plaster
    C) Stone
    D) Plaster

13. A patient requires antibiotic prophylaxis for her surgical extraction. When should she take her medication?
    A) 24 hours before
    B) 12 hours before
    C) 1 hour before
    D) At the time of her appointment.

14. A patient with moderate marginal inflammation should use what type of brushing method?
    A) Fones
    B) Bass
    C) Scrub
    D) Circular

15. Xylitol is a 5-carbon sugar that helps disrupt the development of what bacteria?
    A) S. Mutans
    B) Lactobacillus
    C) Veillonella
    D) Gingivalis

16. A diabetic patient experiences very low blood sugar levels during her appointment. What type of sugar from the emergency drug kit would be appropriate to give her?
   A) Orange juice
   B) Soda
   C) Cake icing
   D) Any of the above

17. A patient on an aspirin regimen might expect what to happen during an extraction?
   A) Inadequate clot formation
   B) Hypersensitivity
   C) Anemia
   D) Excessive bleeding

18. What form lists the risks and precautions associated with a specific chemical?
   A) OSHA Forms
   B) MSDS Sheets
   C) HIPPAA Forms
   D) Ledgers

19. Which of the following is not a procedure under the assistants duties?
   A) Impressions for bite guards
   B) Trimming and cementing of a temporary crown
   C) Cementing of a permanent crown
   D) Fabrication of a whitening tray

20. Bisecting the angle places the x-ray beam at a:
   A) 45 degree angle to the long axis of the tooth
   B) 90 degree angle to the film
   C) 90 degree angle to the imaginary angle between the tooth and the film
   D) 45 degree angle to the imaginary angle between the tooth and the film

21. Which of the following is not true regarding lead foil use in x-rays?
    A) It should be considered biohazardous
    B) It prevents excess radiation exposure to the patient
    C) It should be separated from the film waste
    D) It can leave a mark on the film if it is exposed backward

22. What kVp setting should be used for a child?
    A) 60
    B) 87
    C) 90
    D) 70

23. What is the best way to prevent contaminating a daylight loader?
    A) Wiping down used intraoral films
    B) Placing the films into the loader through the lid
    C) Removing waste through the arm sleeves
    D) Placing the films into a cup and then through the arm sleeves

24. Maxillary radiographs typically have:
    A) Positive angulation of 20-45 degrees
    B) Negative angulation of -20 to -45 degrees
    C) Negative angulation of 0 to -20 degrees
    D) Positive angulation of 0-20 degrees

25. When taking a PA of #13, which exposure technique would not be recommended?
    A) Paralleling technique
    B) Use of a film mounting or placement device
    C) Bisecting the angle
    D) Use of an XCP

26. The proper film processing sequence is:
   A) Wash-developer-wash-fixer
   B) Fixer-wash-developer-rinse
   C) Rinse-developer-fixer-wash
   D) Developer-rinse-fixer-wash

27. The endodontic process cycle on an automatic developer typically takes:
   A) 2 ½ minutes
   B) 90 seconds
   C) 1 minute
   D) 5 minutes

28. What causes a crackled or lighting shaped appearance on a processed film?
   A) Light leaks
   B) Static electricity
   C) Fingernails
   D) Bending the film

29. Which of the following characteristics can aid in the proper mounting of a series of radiographs?
   A) A downward curvature of the smile
   B) Maxillary molars have 2 roots
   C) The film dot is facing upward
   D) Maxillary films show the external oblique ridge

30. To reduce radiation exposure to the patient, you should follow which method?
   A) ALARA
   B) ALAFP
   C) ALAP
   D) ALAYC

31. The effective dose of radiation is known as:
    A) RAD
    B) kVp
    C) mA
    D) REM

32. The operator should stand how far away from the tube head?
    A) 5 feet
    B) 6 feet
    C) 8 feet
    D) Behind a lead wall

33. To minimize secondary exposure, the operatory should stand at what angle to the tube head?
    A) 90-135 degrees
    B) 180 degrees
    C) 45-89 degrees
    D) 0-45 degrees

34. Which of the following are not visible in a periapical x-ray?
    A) Supranumerary teeth
    B) Abscesses
    C) Periodontal disease
    D) TMJ disorders

35. Which fluid is considered to be potentially infectious?
    A) Urine
    B) Sweat
    C) Saliva
    D) Vomit

36. Which of the following follows the best method of hand hygiene?
    A) Washing hands with soap, followed by an alcohol hand rub
    B) Using a foot activated water faucet
    C) Turning the faucet on and off using over gloves
    D) Using alcohol hand rubs when hands are visibly soiled

37. Which of the following diseases should healthcare providers be vaccinated against?
    A) Hepatitis B
    B) Hepatitis C
    C) Tuberculosis
    D) All of the above

38. The "Chain of Infection" consists of:
    A) Portal of entry, virulence, avenue of transmission, susceptibility
    B) Avenue of transmission, susceptibility, number of microorganisms, virulence
    C) Virulence, number of microorganisms, susceptibility, portal of entry
    D) Number of microorganisms, susceptibility, portal of entry, avenue of transmission

39. A dental assistant picks up a tray holding used instruments, and transfers it to another room without using gloves. This is an example of:
    A) Direct contact
    B) Indirect ontact
    C) Bloodborne transmission
    D) Splatter transmission

40. Which of the following is not necessary to maintain an aseptic condition?
    A) Using disposable supplies
    B) Decontamination of charts
    C) Wearing overgloves to write notes during treatment
    D) Avoiding unnecessary touch of other objects

41. What order should your PPE be removed in?
    A) Gloves, mask, coat, eyewear
    B) Eyewear, mask, gloves, coat
    C) Mask, eyewear, gloves, coat
    D) Gloves, eyewear, mask, coat

42. Which of the following instruments is considered semi-critical?
    A) Scalpel
    B) XCP Positioning Ring
    C) Mouth Mirror
    D) Curette

43. Which type of sterilization monitoring is used to indicate that the sterilization machine has reached the proper temperature?
    A) Physical
    B) Chemical
    C) Integrator
    D) Biological

44. Using one tuberculocidal wipe to clean an entire treatment room:
    A) Is completely adequate for the removal of pathogenic microorganisms.
    B) Is not appropriate as a tuberculocidal spray must be used.
    C) Can result in the spread of microorganisms like MRSA.
    D) Cleans areas that are not covered by plastic barriers.

45. Amalgam fillings and lead foil are considered what type of waste?
    A) Hazardous
    B) Infectious
    C) Contaminated
    D) General

46. The federal organization set up to ensure the safety of employees under the direction of the US Department of Labor is:
    A) HIPAA
    B) CDC
    C) OSHA
    D) Worker's Comp

47. What standard is set in place to protect employees from bloodborne diseases like HBV, HCV, and HIV?

    A) Universal precautions standard

    B) Standard precautions standard

    C) Aseptic technique standard

    D) Bloodborne pathogens standard

48. What information is kept in a central location and explains the risks associated with the exposure to chemical substances?

    A) MSDS sheets

    B) Employee vaccination file

    C) OSHA documentaiton

    D) CDC poster

49. What type of infection can lay dormant in the host and produce symptoms that come and go over time?

    A) Opportunistic

    B) Latent

    C) Chronic

    D) Acute

50. After a possible exposure to HIV, the employee must have testing conducted:

    A) Only once after the exposure

    B) Twice after the exposure

    C) Three times after the exposure

    D) Four times after the exposure

51. The permanent dentition has how many teeth?

    a. 20

    b. 30

    c. 36

    d. 42

52. The American Dental Association uses which numbering system?
    a. Universal Numbering System
    b. International Standards System
    c. Palmer Notation System
    d. WHO Numbering System

53. The 3 stages of tooth formation are the:
    a. Zygote, Bell, Eruption
    b. Zygote, Fetal, Infant
    c. Bud, Cap, Eruption
    d. Bud, Cap, Bell

54. Each crown has ___ surfaces.
    a. 6
    b. 5
    c. 4
    d. 7

55. The 3 sets of salivary glands are the:
    a. Wharton's, Stensen's, Bartholin's
    b. Lingual, Parotid, Submandibular
    c. Sublingual, Parotid, Submandibular
    d. Buccal, Sublingual, Parotid

56. Which form of disease is reversible?
    a. Gingivitis
    b. Periodontal disease
    c. Overt decay
    d. Rampant decay

57. The ABCs of assessing possible skin pathologies include:
    a. Asymmetry, Border, Color, Diameter
    b. Asymmetry, Border, Changing, Diameter
    c. Area, Border, Color, Definition
    d. Area, Border, Color, Definition

58. Needed composite restorations are charted by:
    a. Outlining the area in black
    b. Filling the area in using a red pen or pencil
    c. Outlining the area in red
    d. Filling the area in using a black pen

59. A periodontal probe records pocket depths in units of:
    a. Centimeters
    b. Millimeters
    c. Inches
    d. Probing units

60. Average respiration rates in a healthy adult patient is:
    a. 10-15 breaths per minute
    b. 20-30 breaths per minute
    c. Less than 20 breaths per minute
    d. 12-20 breaths per minute

61. What patient position is used for medical emergencies and places the patient's head lower than their knees?
    a. Supine
    b. Sub-supine
    c. Upright
    d. Flat

62. What area serves as a rest for the practitioner's working hand, while also improving stability?
    a. Fulcrum
    b. Stabilizer
    c. Opposing tooth
    d. Patient's chin

63. Viewing the working area through the reflection of a mirror is called:
    a. Reflective vision
    b. Direct vision
    c. Indirect vision
    d. Blind instrumentation

64. What ingredient in local anesthetics helps the anesthesia last longer?
    a. Epinephrine
    b. Lidocaine
    c. Water
    d. Vasoconstrictors

65. Oxygen tanks are:
    a. Blue
    b. Green
    c. White
    d. Yellow

66. What classification of bite indicates an overbite?
    a. I
    b. II
    c. III
    d. IV

67. Which dental specialty focuses on the treatment of diseased dental nerve tissue?
    a. Endodontics
    b. Periodontics
    c. Oral Surgery
    d. Prosthodontics

68. A stainless steel grown is a form of:
    a. Permanent crown
    b. Temporary crown
    c. Lab fabricated crown
    d. Durable crown

69. Which term refers to a patient that is missing all of their teeth?
    a. Mixed dentition
    b. Partially edentulous
    c. Edentulous
    d. Geriatric

70. What is used to recreate the relationship between the upper and lower arches?
    a. Upper and lower plaster models
    b. Bite registration
    c. Die stone
    d. Final impressions

71. What is placed on a prepared tooth under the restoration to protect the nerve from irritation?
    a. Liner
    b. Varnish
    c. Bases
    d. Bonding

72. Which of the following restorations is not a direct restoration?
    a. Amalgam
    b. Composite
    c. Glass ionomers
    d. Gold crown

73. The process of material hardening during the placement of a restorative treatment is called:
    a. Curing
    b. Polymerization
    c. Fixing
    d. Bonding

74. Which cement must be mixed on a glass slab?
    a. Zinc phosphate
    b. Polybycarbonate
    c. Glass ionomers
    d. Resin

75. In the paralleling technique, the preferred film mount system does not include:
    a. Bite block
    b. Snap-a-ray
    c. Locator ring
    d. Indicator arm

76. The locator ring should be placed:
    a. As close to the patient's cheek as possible
    b. As far from the patient's cheek as possible
    c. As parallel to the patient's cheek as possible
    d. As perpendicular to the patient's cheek as possible

77. The most commonly used intraoral film speeds are:
    a. A&D
    b. C&D
    c. D&E
    d. B&D

78. A short tubehead cylinder is how long?
    a. 16"
    b. 8"
    c. 6"
    d. 4"

79. The x-ray beam is restricted to _____ inches to reduce patient radiation.
    a. 2"
    b. 2.6"
    c. 3.4"
    d. 4"

80. The aluminum filter inside of the x-ray tubehead helps remove:
   a. Weak waves
   b. Strong waves
   c. Crooked waves
   d. Short waves

81. The control panel on an x-ray tubehead typically has an mA setting between:
   a. 5-7 mA
   b. 7-12 mA
   c. 10-15 mA
   d. 12-17 mA

82. Which piece of equipment is placed over the patient's neck during radiographs?
   a. Lead apron
   b. Thyroid collar
   c. Patient bib
   d. PPE

83. Maxillary films are best taken with the patient's _____ parallel to the floor.
   a. Nasal-tragus line
   b. Philtrum-tragus line
   c. Orbital-tragus line
   d. Ala-tragus line

84. The up and down position of the x-ray beam is called:
   a. Horizontal angulation
   b. Parallel angulation
   c. Vertical angulation
   d. Lateral angulation

85. Which film records the long axis of the tooth including the apical area of the root?
   a. Periapical
   b. Occlusal
   c. Bitewing
   d. Panoramic

86. What films show the profile of the patient's skull?
     a. Panoramic
     b. Cephalometric
     c. Occlusal
     d. Bitewing

87. If the film is too far away from the tooth, a(n) _____ will exist:
     a. Cone cut
     b. Overlap
     c. Penumbra
     d. Distortion

88. Masks should be discarded:
     a. Twice each day
     b. When splatter is visible
     c. Every 30 minutes
     d. After each patient

89. Which piece of PPE protects the practitioner from inhaling aerosols?
     a. Eyewear
     b. Masks
     c. Gloves
     d. Shields

90. Regarding PPE, gloves:
     a. Prevent the need for hand washing
     b. Should always be made of latex
     c. Prevent cross-contamination
     d. Should be preceded and followed by hand washing

91. Which of the following is not a bloodborne disease?
     a. Hepatitis B
     b. Hepatitis C
     c. Tuberculosis
     d. HIV

92. Transmission of pathogens that are relevant to dental providers include:
    a. Parenteral, bloodborne, direct, indirect, airborne, aerosol
    b. Bloodborne only
    c. Bloodborne and airborne only
    d. Bloodborne, airborne and aerosol only

93. Touching something contaminated with a pathogen is an example of:
    a. Direct contact
    b. Indirect contact
    c. Cross-contamination
    d. The need for PPE

94. Transmission of pathogens through a puncture or cut is an example of:
    a. Bloodborne
    b. Direct
    c. Indirect
    d. Parenteral

95. Disposable equipment helps the dental office by:
    a. Omitting reusable equipment that is difficult to clean
    b. Streamlining patient care
    c. Reducing overhead expenses
    d. Making set-up easier

96. An example of a non-critical instrument would include:
    a. Mirror
    b. Bite block
    c. Spatula
    d. Scaler

97. The types of appropriate sterilization equipment in a dental office include:
    a. Autoclaves and Chemiclaves
    b. Autoclaves, Chemiclaves and Flash Sterilization
    c. Autoclaves and Flash Sterilization
    d. Autoclaves and Cold Sterile Solutions

98. Flash sterilization takes approximately _____ minutes.
   a. 3
   b. 7
   c. 10
   d. 15

99. Autoclaves typically operate at how much pressure?
   a. 10 psi
   b. 15 psi
   c. 25 psi
   d. 50 psi

100. Some cold sterilization immersion may take as long as:
   a. 1 hour
   b. 6 hours
   c. 10 hours
   d. 24 hours

Practice Test Answer Key

1. D
2. D
3. B
4. B
5. D
6. C
7. A
8. D
9. C
10. A
11. B
12. A
13. C
14. B
15. A
16. D
17. D
18. B
19. C
20. C
21. A
22. D
23. B
24. A

25. C
26. D
27. A
28. B
29. C
30. A
31. D
32. B
33. A
34. D
35. C
36. B
37. A
38. C
39. B
40. B
41. D
42. C
43. A
44. C
45. A
46. C
47. D
48. A
49. B
50. D

51. C

52. A

53. D

54. B

55. C

56. A

57. A

58. C

59. B

60. D

61. B

62. A

63. C

64. D

65. B

66. B

67. A

68. B

69. C

70. B

71. A

72. D

73. B

74. A

75. B

76. A

77. C
78. B
79. B
80. A
81. C
82. B
83. D
84. C
85. A
86. B
87. C
88. D
89. B
90. D
91. C
92. A
93. B
94. D
95. A
96. C
97. B
98. A
99. B
100. C

CDA Essential Test Tips DVD
from Trivium Test Prep!

Dear Customer,

Thank you for purchasing from Trivium Test Prep! We're honored to help you prepare for your CDA.

To show our appreciation, we're offering a **FREE *CDA Essential Test Tips* DVD by Trivium Test Prep**. Our DVD includes 35 test preparation strategies that will make you successful on the CDA. All we ask is that you email us your feedback and describe your experience with our product. Amazing, awful, or just so-so: we want to hear what you have to say!

To receive your **FREE *CDA Essential Test Tips* DVD**, please email us at 5star@triviumtestprep.com. Include "Free 5 Star" in the subject line and the following information in your email:

1. The title of the product you purchased.
2. Your rating from 1 – 5 (with 5 being the best).
3. Your feedback about the product, including how our materials helped you meet your goals and ways in which we can improve our products.
4. Your full name and shipping address so we can send your FREE *CDA Essential Test Tips* DVD.

If you have any questions or concerns please feel free to contact us directly at 5star@triviumtestprep.com. Thank you!

- Trivium Test Prep Team

CPSIA information can be obtained
at www.ICGtesting.com
Printed in the USA
LVHW061415150223
739354LV00007B/1010